# A
# WRITER'S
# YEAR

HarperCollins*Publishers*
1 London Bridge Street
London SE1 9GF
www.harpercollins.co.uk

First published by HarperCollins*Publishers* in 2019

10 9 8 7 6 5 4 3 2 1

Copyright © 2019 HarperCollins*Publishers*

Emma Bastow asserts the moral right to be identified
as the author of this work

Text by Emma Bastow
Design by e-Digital Design

A catalogue record for this book is available from the British Library

ISBN 978-0-00-836493-9

Printed and bound in China

# A
# WRITER'S
# YEAR

## 365 CREATIVE
## WRITING PROMPTS

# About the Author

Emma Bastow lives by the sunny south coast of England, where she is lucky enough to combine her passion for creative writing with a career as a freelance editor. When she's not playing with words or lost in the pages of a book, she can be found skipping stones at the beach with her young son, cooking up a storm in the kitchen, and wandering the lanes of Brighton.

*For Tom, may you always be a Rescue Ranger.*

# Introduction

What does creative writing mean to you? I once read that creative writing is "the art of making things up." While this is true, it's also much more. Writing with imagination can take us on a journey—to distant lands, to unexpected places, and even to discover more about ourselves. Creative writing can enthrall, entertain, enchant, and perhaps even make us feel a little uncomfortable. Whether you are writing for fun, for publication, or for your eyes only, here you will find prompts to inspire your daily jottings and banish the fear of the blank page.

## How to use this book

In the following pages, you will find 365 prompts for every mood. You may like to work through the book methodically, allocating time each day to your writing. Or you might prefer to flick through the book at random, developing the ideas that take your fancy. However you choose to use this book, allow your imagination to run wild, your pen to flow freely, and most importantly be kind to yourself and move on to another prompt if the words just won't come—with 365 prompts to choose from, there's bound to be an idea a few pages away that will better suit you in this moment.

## Getting started

Whether you are a seasoned creative writer looking for inspiration, or are just beginning to dabble, allow the prompts in this book to take you on an exciting journey. If you're used to writing short stories, why not seek out the prompts for poetry or film plots. If you're naturally drawn to science fiction, try writing a comedy or romance. You'll see that inspiration can come from the unlikeliest places—desk drawers, junk mail, and everyday household items may not be the most likely sources—but try to look beyond the obvious and use words to turn the mundane into the wonderful.

## Types of creative writing

Creative writing comes in many forms. At the back of this journal, you will find a brief explanation of the terms used in this book. Some are expected—novels, stories, poems, for example—and some may be a little surprising. An obituary or a sales pitch may not spring to mind as an obvious piece of imaginative writing, yet both require a degree of thought, embellishment, and inventive language. To merely present facts in these cases would likely lead to a fairly dull tribute to someone no longer with us, and ineffective marketing of a product or idea.

## Next steps

Think about what you truly want to write. Are you itching to develop a stand-up comedy routine, author a dystopian novel for young adults, or pen lyrical verse for the under-fives? Wherever your passion lies, make this the year that you take the next steps. Perhaps that play you've always wanted to write will find its way to a director, or the sonnets you've been scribbling in your spare time will appear in print. Whatever your reasons for writing creatively, may your work bring you joy, amusement, and enlightenment.

Look up at the sky. What is the weather like today?

_____

_____

_____

_____

_____

_____

_____

What can't you leave the house without?

_____

_____

_____

_____

_____

_____

_____

Stop the clock. What time of day is it? What are you usually doing at this time of day? Do you do this at the same time each day?

Imagine a society ruled solely by children under the age of ten.
What might the laws be?

Open a newspaper and point to a word at random. Repeat three times, now write a sonnet incorporating these three words.

You have the opportunity to move into the apartment of your dreams rent-free, but you have to share it with your worst college roommate. Do you go for it and, if so, what house rules would you set?

You've been elected as leader of your affiliated political party. What do you say in your maiden speech?

You've won an Oscar for playing the lead in your favorite movie.
Write an acceptance speech.

Write an ode to a chair.

_____

_____

_____

_____

_____

_____

_____

What do cats dream about?

_____

_____

_____

_____

_____

_____

_____

_____

Write a transcript for a job interview where the interviewer keeps pausing to take personal phone calls.

You walk into a mall and see that everyone around you is naked. How do you react?

You are a crime detective in the 1800s. What sort of crimes might you be investigating? What resources would be available to you?

Imagine if you had to put all of the objects that are important to you in a box and lock it away for a week. How would you cope?

Write the opening page of a romance novel with a deceitful main character.

Turn on the radio. Write down the first sentence you hear. Turn the radio off again and write a paragraph incorporating this sentence.

Think about going tech-free. How long could you manage for? A day? A week? What would be better and worse about your life if all of the tech suddenly vanished?

You're floating on the ocean. How do you feel?

_____

_____

_____

_____

_____

_____

_____

Write a superhero's to-do list.

_____

_____

_____

_____

_____

_____

_____

_____

Write a eulogy to someone you admire.

Imagine you've been given an unlimited amount of money to spend on a vacation. Where would you travel to and why? Who would you take with you?

If you could travel back in time and meet your younger self, what would you tell them about the future and what would you hold back?

What was the first thing you did on waking this morning? Do you do the same thing every morning? Why?

Write down the first five words you hear next. Think about an alternative meaning for them.

What is your most viewed webpage? What does this say about you?

_____

_____

_____

_____

_____

_____

_____

What do you most fear?

_____

_____

_____

_____

_____

_____

_____

_____

Someone who broke your heart wants to hook up. Do you meet them?

_____

_____

_____

_____

_____

_____

_____

How would you save the World?

_____

_____

_____

_____

_____

_____

_____

Put a pin in a map. Use this as a location for a short horror story.

Think about a teacher who inspired you. What would you say to them if they walked through the door right now?

You are walking through a field lush with crops and wildlife. Imagine you are suddenly very small—what can you see? How different would your outlook be?

You win a major sporting tournament and a TV reporter asks for an interview. Write a transcript for how the conversation might go.

# Describe your worst ever dream.

_____

_____

_____

_____

_____

_____

_____

# Is social media good or bad?

_____

_____

_____

_____

_____

_____

_____

Select "shuffle" on your music player and write a short story based on the first song title selected.

You are about to appear on stage but have forgotten your lines. The play is about a family argument and the lead character has just announced that they are leaving. Write the next scene.

You are caught traveling on public transportation without a ticket. How do you convince the guard not to fine you?

Write a plot outline for a sci-fi movie set a thousand years in the future.

Describe the color yellow.

What are you scared of and why?

What has been the greatest medical advance during your lifetime? How has this changed people's lives?

Write your own obituary.

A huge storm is about to hit your town. The local authorities are advising evacuation. Do you stay or go? What happens next?

Write a letter to someone you want to thank.

If you could change one thing about your personality, what would it be?

Imagine that you have to swap places with a member of your family and live their life for a week. What would you like and dislike? What would you miss about your own life and what would you prefer about theirs?

Describe your favorite food in no more than five words.

_____

_____

_____

_____

_____

_____

_____

A stranger insults you. What do you say to them?

_____

_____

_____

_____

_____

_____

_____

Write a Haiku about a frog.

_____

_____

_____

_____

_____

_____

_____

What does beauty mean to you?

_____

_____

_____

_____

_____

_____

_____

Write a brutally honest dating app entry for your partner or a close friend.

If you could be reincarnated as an animal, which animal would you choose and why? Write about your first day living as that animal.

Think back to a time when you've felt really nervous. What would have helped you to feel more at ease? What would you say to someone feeling that way today?

Write a real-estate ad for your home.

Listen in on a stranger's conversation. Try to build a picture of the people speaking—where they live, work, and their interests. Make them characters in a short story.

Imagine you are standing under a tree. Think about what you can see and hear—how the branches intertwine, the pattern of the bark, and the sound of the leaves moving in the wind. Now write a list of ten adjectives you would use to describe a tree to someone who has never seen one.

Write a letter to someone who has hurt your feelings.

If you could live your life inside a movie, which one would you choose?

_____

_____

_____

_____

_____

_____

_____

_____

You find $1,000 on the street. What do you do with it?

_____

_____

_____

_____

_____

_____

_____

_____

You meet someone who has strong opposing views to you on something you consider important. How do you persuade them to value your opinion?

Describe your perfect death.

Develop a character outline for the lead protagonist in the novel you've always wanted to write.

Write an original joke. Say it out loud then test it on someone else to see if it amuses them.

Write a speech advocating the use of green energy.

A stranger asks what you do. How do you reply?

_____

_____

_____

_____

_____

_____

_____

What's on your bucket list?

_____

_____

_____

_____

_____

_____

_____

_____

Two strangers meet on a stairwell. Neither can pass until one moves out of the way, but both are stubbornly refusing to budge.
What happens next?

You're in a desert in searing heat with no idea which way to travel for water and shelter. What do you do?

Write an alternative ending to your favorite novel.

A bill has been passed to allow doctors to clone humans. How do you feel about this? Would you like to be cloned?

Think about your hometown. Do you still live there? If so, what has kept you there? If not, what made you leave?

List the first five things that come to mind when you read the following words:

| Love | Hate |
|------|------|
| | |

| Resentment | Sadness |
|------------|---------|
| | |

Write the opening scene to a movie set at a point in the future when the Earth has become uninhabitable.

How do you persuade someone to like you?

What would you most like to find in an attic?

_____

_____

_____

_____

_____

_____

_____

Write a list of everyone you respect.

_____

_____

_____

_____

_____

_____

_____

_____

A friend confesses a terrible crime. You are the only person they've told. Do you report it or keep quiet?

Pick a music genre you dislike and write song lyrics in this style.

You have the power to become invisible, but only for an hour a day. How do you spend that hour?

Write an advertisement for a stick of glue.

Think about someone who makes you feel good. What is it about their personality that you find appealing?

You are watching a B movie where sea creatures have evolved into intelligent beings capable of ruling the Earth. The picture freezes five minutes before the end. Write the closing scene.

It's your last day on Earth. Write about how you'll spend it, who with, and where you'll go.

It's almost fall—the leaves are browning, the temperature is dropping, and the days are getting shorter. Are you excited about the coming season or longing for the warmth of summer?

# What personality trait do you most admire?

_____

_____

_____

_____

_____

_____

_____

# What superpower would you choose and why?

_____

_____

_____

_____

_____

_____

_____

_____

If you had to lose one of your senses, which one would you choose?

_____

_____

_____

_____

_____

_____

_____

Someone asks how you are today. How do you reply?

_____

_____

_____

_____

_____

_____

_____

_____

Imagine you are a fish swimming in the ocean. What obstacles and danger might you encounter? How will you find food and safety?

You hate your best friend's new partner. They are besotted. Do you pretend to like them or come clean?

You have been asked to give a presentation to a large group of people on something you know nothing about. How do you hide your ignorance and make them believe in you?

You are living in a post-apocalyptic land where self-sufficiency is the only option. How would you fare? What would your daily routine look like?

Write a stand-up comedy routine on the theme of death.

The government rules that all books must be destroyed. Write a protest chant.

Think about a novel you've read that has been made into a movie.
Did you prefer the novel or the movie? Did the plot alter at all?
If so, why may the plot have been altered for the screen?

# What gives you joy?

_____

_____

_____

_____

_____

_____

_____

# What makes someone a good person?

_____

_____

_____

_____

_____

_____

_____

_____

You arrive home to find your apartment has been burglarized and everything you own has been taken. Who do you call for help?

It's a summer's day. The sun is warming your skin and you can smell flowers all around you. What emotions do you feel?

Look out of the window. Look beyond the things you notice every day and try to focus on the details. Describe what you can see.

You can spend a day with anyone in the World. Who do you choose and where do you go?

Think back to when you were a child. What did you want to be when you grew up? Write a job advertisement for this role. Would you apply for the job now?

Imagine looking out of a window onto a snowy mountain range. Would you rather enjoy the view from afar or are you itching to explore? What adventures may await?

Think about something that really made you angry. Why was this and what could you do to change it?

List as many uses as you can think of for a cardboard box.

_____

_____

_____

_____

_____

_____

_____

What are you grateful for today?

_____

_____

_____

_____

_____

_____

_____

_____

You've been given the opportunity to join the maiden expedition to a recently discovered planet. What do you pack?

Write a poem about jealousy.

You find a bag in the street and take it home. What's inside is totally unpredictable and has the ability to change your life. What is it?

A friend is about to do something stupid. How do you persuade them not to?

Imagine you were born in a different era. How would your life be different? What privileges and rights available to you now would have been denied then?

The world is suddenly plunged into darkness. The sun is obscured and all artificial lighting fails. Write about how this would impact your life.

Write a manifesto for a fictional political party whose core values differ from your own.

Think about a key decision you've made in your life and imagine if you'd made a different decision. Write about how your life would be different—would it be better or worse? Would you be happier? More successful?

Write an advertisement for a mundane everyday item.

Write a romantic poem to your first love.

_____

_____

_____

_____

_____

_____

_____

List five items you'd save if your house was on fire.

_____

_____

_____

_____

_____

_____

_____

_____

Imagine you are floating on a cloud high above the Earth.
Where would you go?

You are granted three wishes. Each wish can only be used once and not at the same time as another wish. What do you wish for?

Think about your favorite song or piece of music. How does it make you feel when you hear it and what memories does it bring to the surface?

If dogs could talk, what would they say?

You are arrested for a crime you didn't commit. How do you convince the cops that it wasn't you?

A spaceship lands in your backyard. You climb aboard and notice that the destination is Utopia. Do you take off with the ship or stay here on Earth?

Think about a book you have read more than once. What made you re-read it?

Think about someone you dislike. Why is this? What did they do to make you feel this way?

Take a look at the first sentence of the most recent e-mail you received (excluding the greeting). Write a scene using this as a line.

Write a letter to your younger self.

A relative turns up at your home unannounced. It's a really bad time.
Do you tell them or invite them in? Write what follows.

Write a comedy routine based on the most amusing conversation you've ever overheard.

Write down five words to describe a spoon.

_____

_____

_____

_____

_____

_____

_____

Would you prefer to be extremely hot or extremely cold?

_____

_____

_____

_____

_____

_____

_____

_____

Look at any recent junk mail you have received. Can you re-arrange the words to completely change the meaning?

Fill in the blanks to complete the sentence, then develop it into a paragraph: Was it so unbelievable that _____ could have _____? After all it wasn't the first time they had _____.

Write a "Knock Knock" joke.

Imagine you are on a beach. You can feel the sand, hear the ocean, and smell the salty sea water. How would you describe this scene to someone lacking these senses?

List the first letters of eight objects you can see around you. Write a poem, starting each line with words that begin with these letters.

List five uses for a plastic bag. Carrying things cannot be one of them.

_____

_____

_____

_____

_____

_____

_____

_____

What is your best feature?

_____

_____

_____

_____

_____

_____

_____

_____

How would you describe a table to someone who has never seen one?

Astronauts have made contact with life forms on another planet. Representatives are planning on visiting Earth, and you have been asked to write a welcome letter. What would you say?

Write an ad for a self-peeling banana.

What would you most like to automate in your home?

All forms of electronic and written communication are banned for the day. The only way to communicate is by talking. What sort of impact would this have on your professional and personal life?

Write a short crime fiction story that begins with a blind date.

List as many film genres as you can think of.

_____

_____

_____

_____

_____

_____

_____

Are you reliable?

_____

_____

_____

_____

_____

_____

_____

Write the plot for a romantic comedy based on a cruise liner.

You awake to find that your appearance has altered completely. How do you make those around you believe you are still you?

If you could re-live any event in your life, which one would you choose and why?

Write a short story based in a laundromat.

You wake in a hospital bed with no recollection of how you got there. There are no clues as to what may have happened to you or how long you've been there. Write the opening scene of a play based on this scenario.

Write the plot for a horror story set on a high-speed train.

Write a weather report in the style of a children's television character.

What does the word "special" mean to you?

_____

_____

_____

_____

_____

_____

_____

What makes you laugh?

_____

_____

_____

_____

_____

_____

_____

_____

What have you done that might be considered really daring?

_____

_____

_____

_____

_____

_____

_____

_____

What would you most like to be famous for?

_____

_____

_____

_____

_____

_____

_____

_____

Write your full name vertically, with each letter on a separate line.
Think of a word beginning with each letter to describe yourself.

Write a letter to your childhood hero.

You arrive on vacation to find that you have accidentally booked a silent retreat. How long could you be silent for? What feelings and emotions would surface?

Write about the most bizarre love triangle imaginable.

Imagine you are a bird. What secrets would your bird's-eye view enable you to uncover?

You build a time machine. You've worked out how to travel to the past and future, but not how to return to the present. You hope that your future self will have figured this out. Do you time travel anyway?

To whom would you most like to apologize?

_____

_____

_____

_____

_____

_____

_____

What is your dream job and why?

_____

_____

_____

_____

_____

_____

_____

You win a flight to a destination of your choice. Where do you choose to travel to and why? What would you experience in your chosen destination?

Write a break-up letter.

You are alone on a desert island. It's nearing nightfall and you don't have anything to eat or drink. Do you prioritize food, water, or shelter?

Write down five objects beginning with the letter "L." Write a short children's story about these things being lost and found.

Choose a poem you like. Switch out the adjectives to their exact opposites. How does this change the meaning? How do you feel about the poem now?

With whom would you most like to be stuck on a subway train?

_____

_____

_____

_____

_____

_____

_____

List ten green objects.

_____

_____

_____

_____

_____

_____

_____

_____

Write a sonnet with the first letter of each line in alphabetical order.

Write the opening scene to a play where the first line spoken is:
"An onion has many layers."

You notice someone in the street who seems to be in distress. You are late for an important meeting and no one else seems to have noticed. Do you stop and try to help or walk on by? What might happen next?

Write the synopsis for a novel where the plot involves the exposure of a great secret.

Imagine you could swap genders for a day. How would your day differ from usual? Would others treat you differently?

Take a piece of paper and draw whatever you like without giving it too much thought. What did you draw? If your picture was a front cover of a book, what might the book be about?

Your phone rings. Who do you most want to speak to?

_____

_____

_____

_____

_____

_____

_____

_____

What would your specialist subject be in a general knowledge quiz?

_____

_____

_____

_____

_____

_____

_____

_____

Write an article about something that annoys you for your local newspaper.

List five uses for each of the following items:

Hat

Scissors

Paperclip

Bucket

Write the script for a television commercial for a home cleaning product.

A relative has promised you a substantial inheritance on the condition that the money is used to set up a profitable business. Write a business plan to convince your benefactor of your worth.

Write the President's to-do list.

"The whole is greater than the sum of its parts." To what extent is this statement true?

Write down ten words associated with the desert.

How could you be a better version of yourself?

_____

_____

_____

_____

_____

_____

_____

List as many different types of music as you can think of.

_____

_____

_____

_____

_____

_____

_____

_____

You are given the opportunity to appear on your local news program to discuss an issue you feel is important to your community, and to debate with others who feel differently. What topic do you choose?

If you knew when you were going to die, would you live your
life differently?

Write about two people who live together but never meet and only communicate through written notes.

Imagine you are losing your sight. What will you most miss looking at?

Write a comedy about a contract killer who is scared of blood.

Describe your perfect afterlife.

What do you see through rose-tinted glasses?

_____

_____

_____

_____

_____

_____

_____

Why did the chicken cross the road?

_____

_____

_____

_____

_____

_____

_____

Close your eyes and open a drawer in your home or workplace. Select an item and write a murder mystery using this item as the murder weapon.

Write about a surgeon who develops shaky hands.

Start a stopwatch and look away. At a time of your choosing, stop
the timer. Write down the numbers without full points. Imagine the
numbers represent a particular year (e.g. 19.32 seconds becomes the
year 1932). Write about a fictional event that occurred or will occur
in this year.

Write about ten seconds that changed your life.

Write a story where everyone is deliriously happy.

What does success mean to you?

Visit a local library or bookstore. Select a book you aren't familiar with at random and note the title. Write a blurb explaining what the book might be about.

What will be written on your tombstone?

Two cars collide on a remote road. Neither of the drivers are harmed but both cars are badly damaged and there is no cell phone reception. Nightfall is approaching and the temperature is dropping. What happens next?

List five red items.

_____

_____

_____

_____

_____

_____

_____

How do you want to be remembered?

_____

_____

_____

_____

_____

_____

_____

_____

You arrive home to find that a mystery person has moved in. They are convinced that they own your home and have every right to be there. What happens next?

Write a song about a romance between a human and an AI.

You are recruited to spy for the intelligence agencies. What is your first mission?

Write a letter to be read 100 years from now.

Close your eyes and spin around for the count of five. Stop and open your eyes. What is the first thing your eyes focus on? Write an ode to this object.

List every type of emotion you can think of. Pick three and write about three characters who go to the grocery store while each feeling one of these emotions strongly. How might this affect their behavior and choices?

Finish the sentence: "I wish I could..."

_____

_____

_____

_____

_____

_____

_____

_____

What is your greatest achievement?

_____

_____

_____

_____

_____

_____

_____

_____

Write a week's worth of diary entries for a World-famous music star.

Scientists discover a cure for aging, allowing us to choose which age we'd like to be for the rest of our lives. Which age would you choose?

Write a packing list for a trip to the Moon.

Write a completely fictional social media profile for yourself.
What impression would it give about your life?

If you could perform magic, what spells would you cast?

Write a shopping list for a mouse with superpowers.

_____

_____

_____

_____

_____

_____

_____

_____

What is the last thing you do at night?

_____

_____

_____

_____

_____

_____

_____

_____

Write about a bitter rivalry between competing athletes.

What was the last lie you told?

Write a ballad in the style of a country and western singer.

A small child asks you to tell them a tale about a green giant who lives in a cave and is lonely. Write the story.

Look around you—can you see a photograph? If not, imagine an image in your home. Write a fictional scene based around the photograph.

What IS the worst that could happen?

_____

_____

_____

_____

_____

_____

_____

_____

What does "living dangerously" mean to you?

_____

_____

_____

_____

_____

_____

_____

_____

Think about song lyrics you have misheard. Write a short story using the misheard lyrics as a theme.

What charity would you most like to set up and why?

# Write a story with unlikeable characters.

You are on day two of a five-day solo expedition. Your backpack seems to be getting heavier with every step. The backpack contains food, water, your most valuable keepsake, and your cell phone. The only way to lighten the load is to remove one of these items. Which would you choose?

Finish the sentence: "I have never…"

What would you like to be given a second chance at?

_____

_____

_____

_____

_____

_____

_____

What would your biography be called?

_____

_____

_____

_____

_____

_____

_____

_____

_____

Write a wedding speech from the perspective of a jilted groom.

Write a letter to someone you haven't forgiven.

A person is found wandering in a local park. They have lost their memory and have no idea who they are. They are carrying a wallet full of notes of multiple denominations, are dressed in a heavy coat on a warm day, and have tattoos of cartoon characters. Who are they and how did they end up in your local park?

Write a stand-up comedy routine on the theme of extinction.

Who would you like to trade places with and why?

_____

_____

_____

_____

_____

_____

_____

_____

What would take you completely out of your comfort zone?

_____

_____

_____

_____

_____

_____

_____

_____

How would your friends describe you?

_____

_____

_____

_____

_____

_____

_____

What does home mean to you?

_____

_____

_____

_____

_____

_____

_____

_____

Write a slogan for a billboard advertising an award-winning public restroom.

Write down ten words associated with winter.

Write down the name of your favorite store. If you weren't familiar with the store, would the name give any clue as to the type of business? If you were to open a store, what would you call it and why?

Write a short story set at the bottom of the ocean.

Write a menu for a fictional fast-food restaurant.

Think of the number eight. What significance does this number have to you? Does it feature in your current age? Your door or phone number? What appears in eights in the natural world? Write down everything you can think of.

What is your least favorite sound?

_____

_____

_____

_____

_____

_____

_____

What sport would you most like to excel at?

_____

_____

_____

_____

_____

_____

_____

_____

Touch the surface of a metal object. Does it feel smooth or rough? Is it shiny or mat? Curved or flat? Write down as many descriptive words as you can and then incorporate these words into a short story.

Write about a very rich person who loses everything.

Imagine you are out walking. Your mind wanders and you realize that you are lost. Your cell phone is at home and you can't see any other people. Write what happens next.

A chemical attack has forced the surviving inhabitants of Earth to live underground. The younger generation cannot remember what it was like to live on the surface. Explain it to them.

Lie on the ground and look up at the sky. What can you see?

_____

_____

_____

_____

_____

_____

_____

What does mindfulness mean to you?

_____

_____

_____

_____

_____

_____

_____

_____

Write a poem about longing.

A law is passed banning the manufacture and sale of all non-essential items for a year. During this year it will not be possible to purchase clothing, household items, vehicles, or technology. Write about how this would impact your day-to-day life.

Write a rhyme that would appeal to a small child.

Open up your most-used bag. List the contents. If someone found this bag in the street, what would the contents tell them about you?

What do you have too much of?

_____

_____

_____

_____

_____

_____

_____

_____

What would you like more of?

_____

_____

_____

_____

_____

_____

_____

_____

Write a story about someone who wins the lottery but doesn't
tell anyone.

You are asked to give a speech on an issue you feel strongly about. The audience are very likely to have opposing views, and your job is to convince them you are right. How do you achieve this?

List as many words as you can think of that are associated with the following colors:

Violet

Gray

Orange

White

Play a word association game with yourself, starting with the
word "strange."

Listen to a piece of instrumental classical music. Think about how music can tell a story and evoke emotions without the use of language. Now write a short story inspired by the music and how it made you feel.

You wake one day to find that every clock around the world has stopped and there is no way of telling what the time is. Write what happens next.

What secrets have you never told?

_____

_____

_____

_____

_____

_____

_____

If you could go anywhere and do anything at this very moment, what
would you do?

_____

_____

_____

_____

_____

_____

_____

_____

Write a story in which all of the characters have been reincarnated.

You discover that your whole life has been a science experiment. Everyone around you is acting, and your every move has been analyzed. Would you carry on living the life you know or choose to live in the "real" world?

Write the plot for a romantic comedy set in a war zone.

Think about a novel you've always wanted to write. Now imagine this novel is going to be adapted for the stage. Write the opening paragraph to your novel and the opening scene of the play.

Write three statements about yourself that are completely fictional.

Write the following words on separate pieces of paper: soldier, mother, lover, overcoat, sail, danger. Fold the pieces of paper so you can't see the words and place them into a bowl. Choose a piece of paper at random and write a piece using this word as a theme. Repeat for all six words.

Write about forbidden love.

Are the eyes really the window to the soul?

_____

_____

_____

_____

_____

_____

_____

What are you addicted to?

_____

_____

_____

_____

_____

_____

_____

_____

You are embarking on a grueling expedition and can only pack five
personal items. Which items would you choose?

Write a dystopian story set in a parallel universe.

A woman you don't recognize walks into your place of work. She greets you like an old friend. Her presence makes you feel uneasy and you've no recollection of meeting her before. What do you do?

Write about a character whose memory is wiped at the end of each day.

You hear on the news that a dangerous animal has escaped from your local zoo and has been spotted in your neighborhood. Write what happens next.

How risk averse are you?

_____

_____

_____

_____

_____

_____

_____

List every word you can think of associated with stars.

_____

_____

_____

_____

_____

_____

_____

_____

You enter a competition to develop a new animated TV series. The only criteria are that the characters cannot be human. Write your proposal.

Write a story based on the theme: "When life gives you lemons, make lemonade."

Write a review of a restaurant you've never been to.

An airplane crashes on a remote island. Everyone survives but there is no food or water and a rescue attempt will take a few days. What character traits will be beneficial to cope in this situation?

If your life was a video game, what would it be called?

_____

_____

_____

_____

_____

_____

_____

Whose work do you admire and why?

_____

_____

_____

_____

_____

_____

_____

_____

Write a sci-fi story where the enemy can take on the form of surrounding objects.

Look at or visualize a famous work of art. What might have inspired the artist? Why have they chosen to capture this particular scene? What story does the artwork convey?

Write a short story beginning with the line:"Once upon a time…"

You absent-mindedly peer into a window and see something totally unexpected. Describe the scene.

Finish the sentence: "She knew she would never be the same person again after…"

Write a newspaper article about a bar brawl in the Wild West.

Write the most bizarre plot for an opera you can think of.

List as many different types of written media as you can.

_____

_____

_____

_____

_____

_____

_____

What do you do to relax?

_____

_____

_____

_____

_____

_____

_____

_____

Create an advertisement for an umbrella in the style of a
Shakespearean play.

A car is traveling at speed. The occupants are arguing and one is trying to open the door. The car swerves into oncoming traffic and someone screams. Write what has happened to lead the characters up to this point.

Draft a synopsis for a book you think would appeal to the 11–16 age group.

Write the plot outline for a book where the reader is able to choose their own adventure by selecting different scenarios. How many different endings can you come up with?

Which extinct species would you most like to have saved?

Would you like to be immortal?

A woman walks alone in a forest. The path forks at a sign indicating that one way is "Enlightenment" and the other is "Eternal happiness." What happens next?

Write about identical twins who trick everyone into thinking they are one person.

As a measure designed to expose criminals, the authorities have begun adding truth serum to drinking water, meaning that everyone cannot help but tell the truth at all times. Write about a society with no lies or deception.

Pen a poem on the theme of wrath.

Where would you like to escape to?

_____

_____

_____

_____

_____

_____

_____

When did you last cheat?

_____

_____

_____

_____

_____

_____

_____

You arrive home to find that your furniture has been re-arranged. There's no sign of forced entry and no one else has access to your home. What do you do?

Write a short story about a missing person.

Imagine you are being chased. You're running as fast as you can but don't seem able to get away. You reach a dead end and can feel your pursuer getting close. Describe what happens next.

Write a joke about a shopkeeper and a thief.

What is the biggest mistake you've ever made?

_____

_____

_____

_____

_____

_____

_____

_____

Write the worst pun you can think of.

_____

_____

_____

_____

_____

_____

_____

_____

_____

Write a letter to your future self, to be opened ten years from now.
What will your life be like? What do you hope to have achieved?

You find yourself trapped in a museum overnight. What do you do?

Write about a chance encounter at an airport.

Dinosaurs are back on Earth, and they want their planet back.
Describe the almighty war that ensues.

What's the strangest phobia you can think of?

_____

_____

_____

_____

_____

_____

_____

What should you really own up to?

_____

_____

_____

_____

_____

_____

_____

Who would you like to bring back from the dead?

_____

_____

_____

_____

_____

_____

_____

What's behind the magic door?

_____

_____

_____

_____

_____

_____

_____

_____

Finish the sentence: "The sun shone so brightly, but still he couldn't see…"

Write about two people who cannot understand each other.

Pen the opening lines of a play about an insomniac living in Ancient Greece.

A large rabbit knocks at your door and asks to come in for a drink. Do you oblige?

List every word you can think of that contains the letter "X."

_____

_____

_____

_____

_____

_____

_____

_____

Write a rhyme about a slug.

_____

_____

_____

_____

_____

_____

_____

_____

You buy an antique photo frame from a thrift store and discover a secret message scrawled on the back. What does it say?

Write about a case of mistaken identity.

Write about the breakdown of a relationship following misread text messages.

You are caught snooping in a friend's closet. How do you convince them you were just looking for something?

Write an ode to a pen.

_____

_____

_____

_____

_____

_____

_____

_____

What makes you nervous?

_____

_____

_____

_____

_____

_____

_____

_____

_____

Your therapist starts sobbing uncontrollably. What do you do?

Write a story where the opening paragraph gives the ending away.

If your walls could talk, what stories would they tell?

You board a bus and soon notice that every other passenger is having an animated conversation with themselves. What happens next?

List five uses for a paper cup.

_____

_____

_____

_____

_____

_____

_____

What is the longest word you can think of?

_____

_____

_____

_____

_____

_____

_____

_____

Describe a major world event from the perspective of a seven-year-old child.

Write a story that ends with the line: "And then he woke up."

Using only dialogue, write about a reunion that goes horribly wrong.

Write a serial killer's shopping list.

Write down the colors of the rainbow, then list a character trait that suits each color.

_____

_____

_____

_____

_____

_____

_____

_____

What's your biggest waste of time?

_____

_____

_____

_____

_____

_____

_____

_____

Your boss declines your request to take leave for a vacation you've already paid for. Do you go anyway and try to avoid being found out?

You enter a room to find everyone laughing hysterically.
What's so funny?

Write about a couple who have a very different perspective on a shared memory.

You hire a private investigator to spy on your partner, only to find that the investigator is also spying on you. Write what happens next.

## What's the best piece of advice you've ever been given?

## List every item on your desk.

Write about a person who fakes their own death.

You visit a remote island connected to the mainland by a bridge. During your stay, the bridge is closed due to bad weather, cutting off the island and its inhabitants. One by one the islanders begin to vanish, until you are the only person left. Where did everyone go?

Draft the plot for a zombie movie set in a health spa.

Finish the sentence: "If money was no object…"

Write about a day in the life of a ghost.

# Glossary

**Advertisement**: Marketing communication aimed at selling a particular service, product, or event.

**Article**: Non-fiction writing typically appearing with others in a newspaper or magazine.

**Eulogy**: Often in the form of a speech given at a funeral, a eulogy praises an individual, acknowledging the importance of their life and their legacy.

**Haiku**: A short verse of three non-rhyming lines with five, seven, and five syllables. Originating in Japan, traditionally a haiku will depict an image from nature.

**Novel**: Long narrative prose about fictional characters and events.

**Novella**: Fictional narrative prose that is longer than a short story but shorter than a novel.

**Obituary**: A written piece, typically appearing in a newspaper, announcing someone's death and giving an overview of that person's life.

**Ode**: A lyrical poem praising or glorifying an object, event, or person.

**Play**: A theatrical performance usually consisting of dialogue between characters.

**Plot**: The storyline of a play, movie, or novel, typically written as a series of events.

**Rhyme**: Rhyming poetry, typically with rhyming words at the end of lines, often with a comedic element.

**Serial**: A play, television show, or publication appearing in regular instalments.

**Script**: The spoken element of a play, movie, or broadcast.

**Short story**: Fictional prose that can be read in one sitting.

**Sonnet**: A poem of 14 lines, each with ten syllables. A Shakespearean sonnet typically has three four-lined stanzas called "quatrains" followed by a two-line stanza called a "couplet."